THE INDI[...] THE CUPBOARD

STUDY GUIDE

by Andrew Clausen

Progeny Press

Limited permission to reproduce this study guide.

Purchase of this study guide entitles an individual teacher
to reproduce pages for use in the classroom or home.
Multiple teachers may not reproduce pages
from the same study guide.

The Indian in the Cupboard Study Guide
A Progeny Press Study Guide
by Andrew Clausen
edited by Michael Gilleland
cover design by Michael Gilleland

Printed in the United States of America.

ISBN 978-1-58609-338-9 Book
       978-1-58609-565-9 CD
       978-1-58609-430-0 Set

Table of Contents

Note to Instructor

How to Use Progeny Press Study Guides. Progeny Press study guides are designed to help students better understand and enjoy literature by getting them to notice and understand how authors craft their stories and to show them how to think through the themes and ideas introduced in the stories. To properly work through a Progeny Press study guide, students should have easy access to a good dictionary, a thesaurus, a Bible (we use NIV translation, but that is up to your preference; just be aware of some differences in language), and sometimes a topical Bible or concordance. Supervised access to the Internet also can be helpful at times, as can a good set of encyclopedias.

Most middle grades and high school study guides take from eight to ten weeks to complete, generally working on one section per week. Over the years, we have found that it works best if the students completely read the novel the first week, while also working on a prereading activity chosen by the parent or teacher. Starting the second week, most parents and teachers have found it works best to work on one study guide page per day until the chapter sections are completed. Students should be allowed to complete questions by referring to the book; many questions require some cross-reference between elements of the stories.

Most study guides contain an Overview section that can be used as a final test, or it can be completed in the same way the chapter sections were completed. If you wish to perform a final test but your particular study guide does not have an Overview section, we suggest picking a couple of questions from each section of the study guide and using them as your final test.

Most study guides also have a final section of essays and postreading activities. These may be assigned at the parents' or teachers' discretion, but we suggest that students engage in several writing or other extra activities during the study of the novel to complement their reading and strengthen their writing skills.

As for high school credits, most Christian high schools with whom we have spoken have assigned a value of one-fourth credit to each study guide, and this also seems to be acceptable to colleges assessing homeschool transcripts.

Internet References

All websites listed in this study guide were checked for appropriateness at the time of publication. However, due to the changing nature of the Internet, we cannot guarantee that the URLs listed will remain appropriate or viable. Therefore, we urge parents and teachers to take care in and exercise careful oversight of their children's use of the Internet.

Synopsis

On his birthday, Omri is somewhat disappointed to receive a small plastic Indian from his friend Patrick, but he is pleased when his brother Gillon gives him a white metal cupboard. Omri discovers that a key, once belonging to his great-grandmother, fits the lock on the cupboard perfectly. He puts the plastic Indian in the cupboard for the night and locks the cupboard door.

In the morning Omri is shocked to discover that the cupboard has somehow brought the Indian to life. Keeping it a secret, Omri helps the Indian adjust to his new home in Omri's bedroom, providing him with food and shelter. But Omri learns that the Indian is more than a novelty. He is a real person, an Iroquois brave, he has a name, Little Bear, and he lived in the past over 200 years ago.

But Omri cannot keep Little Bear a secret. He lets Patrick in on the discovery. Patrick does not understand that Little Bear is a real person, not a toy. He demands that Omri use the cupboard to bring a plastic cowboy to life for him. Omri has a hard time convincing the cowboy and Indian to get along, and when Patrick forces Omri to bring the little men to school, neither of them foresees the trouble that results.

About the Author

Lynne Reid Banks was born in London and was evacuated to Saskatchewan, Canada, during World War II. The daughter of an actress, she also developed an interest in acting. She graduated from the Royal Academy of Dramatic Art in London in 1949 and worked as an actress for five years. She later became a journalist and was the first woman reporter on British television.

She emigrated to Israel in 1962 where she lived in a kibbutz and taught English to Hebrew-speaking children. She later returned to London where she writes full-time and occasionally acts on radio. She was married in 1965 and has three children.

Lynne Reid Banks is the author of over 25 books, including some volumes of Jewish history. *The Return of the Indian*, the sequel to *The Indian in the Cupboard*, was a Junior Literary Guild selection. *Dark Quartet: The Story of the Brontës* was named a Best Book for Young Adults by the American Library Association for the year 1977.

Ideas for Pre-reading Activities

1. Find information about the way the Iroquois Indians lived during the 1700s. Where did they live? What did their dwellings look like? What did their clothing look like? What were their customs? What were their religious beliefs? How were they affected by the settlement of North America by Europeans? Discuss these questions in a short paper.

2. Find information about the French and Indian War. Who was fighting whom? What were they fighting over? Which Indians were involved? Whose side were they on? What effect did this war have on the Indians involved? Discuss these questions in a short paper.

Chapters 1 & 2

Vocabulary:

Match the vocabulary words on the left with their definitions on the right.

____ coherent		a.	dejected
____ plait		b.	an ammunition belt worn across the chest
____ bandolier		c.	squirmed
____ intricate		d.	braid
____ row		e.	proudly, arrogantly
____ longhouse		f.	a noisy quarrel
____ crestfallen		g.	resistance
____ writhed		h.	complex
____ defiance		i.	rational
____ haughtily		j.	a communal dwelling

Characterization:

The sentences below give us some insight into Omri's character. After each item, explain what the incident tells you about Omri.

> Example: [Omri wished that] he might pass his spelling test next day, which it would take real magic to bring about as he hadn't even looked at the words.

Omri has very poor study habits.

1. Omri was getting a little fed up with small plastic figures, of which he had loads. Biscuit tinsful, probably three or four if they were all put away at the same time, which they never were because most of the time they were scattered about in the bathroom, the loft, the kitchen, the breakfast room. . . .

2. "And now it's your cupboard key. Please don't lose it, Omri, will you?"

3. There was a stupid row at the breakfast table because Adiel took the last of the Rice Krispies, and although there were plenty of cornflakes, not to mention Sugar Puffs, [Omri and his brother] fairly set upon Adiel and made such an awful fuss that their mother lost her temper.

4. He was so annoyed when he remembered . . . that he turned on Adiel and shouted, "You made me forget my swimming stuff!" and bashed him.

5. Later, after they'd had the spelling test and Omri had been marked three right out of ten. . . .

6. At the very best, the Indian must have passed a horrible day in that dark prison. Omri was appalled at the thought of it.

7. His main concern was to get downstairs without his parents hearing him, get to the kitchen, find some food that would suit the Indian, and bring it back without anyone asking questions.

Questions:

1. How did Omri feel about Patrick's gift? Why?

2. What happened when the plastic Indian was locked in the cupboard?

3. Why did Omri want to keep Little Bear a secret?

Thinking about the Story:

4. Little Bear threatened Omri. Do you think he could have really killed Omri? Explain.

5. Omri wanted to keep Little Bear a secret, yet at the same time he felt a need to talk about it. Why do you think this was?

Dig Deeper:

6. Omri felt that Little Bear was no longer a plaything, but a person who had to be respected no matter how small. Read the following verses. What does each one say about treatment of others?

    Luke 6:31–35—

    Romans 12:10—

    Philippians 2:3—

    1 Peter 2:17—

7. Do you think Omri treated Little Bear as he should according to these verses? Give examples to support your answers.

Chapters 3, 4 & 5

Vocabulary:

A word is *in context* if we see it in the sentence in which it was written. It is *out of context* when it is by itself. The following underlined words are shown in the context of the sentence from the book where they appear. See if you can figure out from reading the sentence what the underlined words mean, then write the meaning from the dictionary.

1. The Indian rose <u>lithely</u> to his feet and jumped off onto the grey carpet.
    Your definition:

    Dictionary definition:

2. He selected a smallish brown horse . . . that had originally carried an Arab, brandishing a curved sword at a <u>platoon</u> of French Foreign Legionnaires.
    Your definition:

    Dictionary definition:

3. Grasping the high <u>pommel</u> of the saddle, he swung himself into it.
    Your definition:

    Dictionary definition:

4. Omri quickly found a small cardboard box that had held a Matchbox <u>lorry</u>.
    Your definition:

    Dictionary definition:

5. Little Bear was clearly <u>reluctant</u> to return to the house.
    Your definition:

    Dictionary definition:

6. Full of <u>foreboding</u>, Omri bent down and peered into the box.
    Your definition:

    Dictionary definition:

7. The soldier was kneeling at Little Bear's feet, applying a neat <u>tourniquet</u> to the top of his leg.
    Your definition:

    Dictionary definition:

Questions:

1. In the morning, what had happened to the plastic tepee that Omri had put in the cupboard? What had happened to the Matchbox car? Why didn't anything happen the first time Omri put them in the cupboard?

2. Omri is shocked to learn that Little Bear isn't merely a plastic Indian come to life, but a real living person with a history. Why does this bother Omri?

Does this revelation cause any change in the way Omri treats Little Bear? Explain your answer using examples from the story.

3. How does Little Bear get injured?

4. What is Omri's solution for helping the injured Indian?

5. How did Omri get an axe for Little Bear?

Thinking About the Story:

6. Does Little Bear treat Omri as an equal, someone higher that himself (like a god), or someone lower than himself (like a slave or servant)? Cite examples from the story to support your answer.

7. Little Bear figures out that Omri is someone who can do things for him and get him the things he needs. How does he make use of this knowledge?

8. Look through these three chapters and list the things that Little Bear asks Omri to give him.

9. Does Omri give Little Bear everything he asks for? What things *does* he give to Little Bear?

   What things does he refuse to give to Little Bear?

10. When Omri refuses to give Little Bear some things, how does Little Bear react?

Dig Deeper:

11. Sometimes God does not give us the things we ask for. Why do you think this is?

12. Read Psalm 84:11, Matthew 7:11 and 1 John 5:14, 15. What do these verses say about God's willingness to grant our requests?

    What do these verses say about what God requires of us in prayer?

13. Read 2 Corinthians 12:7–10. What did Paul ask of God? What reasons did God give for not granting Paul's request. How did Paul respond?

14. Read Matthew 26:39–44. What did Jesus ask of God? What was the will of God in that situation? How did Jesus respond?

15. Think of a time when you prayed for something that God did not grant. How did you respond? How should you respond when God does not seem to be answering your prayers?

Point of View:

In *The Indian in the Cupboard*, the author is able to help readers see things from Little Bear's point of view by showing how common objects appear to a person of Little Bear's size. Look back through the story and find how the objects listed below appear to Little Bear. In the space next to each object write down the object to which the author makes a comparison.

Example: Omri's dresser _____A big mountain_____

1. Omri's lamp _____

2. The carpet in Omri's bedroom _____

3. Small stones on the path outside _____

4. Weeds _____

5. The edge of the lawn _____

6. The shadow of a passing bird _____

Writing Project:

Omri found that more and more he was able to see things from Little Bear's point of view. For a creative writing exercise, go into your bedroom and imagine how it would appear to someone only three inches tall. Write a page or two describing your bedroom from the point of view of a person Little Bear's size.

Chapters 6 & 7

Vocabulary:

Underline the word on the right that comes closest in meaning to the vocabulary word on the left.

1.	**maize**	carrots	potatoes	corn
2.	**pence**	pennies	paper clips	thumb tacks
3.	**peevish**	sad	frightened	irritable
4.	**dire**	urgent	amusing	surprising
5.	**hector**	intimidate	entertain	reject
6.	**galvanized**	shocked	soothed	settled
7.	**grope**	throw	drop	reach
8.	**agog**	offended	hurt	expectant
9.	**magnanimously**	dramatically	generously	fearfully
10.	**feeble**	rough	weak	stiff
11.	**reek**	noise	odor	flavor

Questions:

1. List three things Omri learns about the Iroquois from the book he found at the library.

2. In handicrafts class, Omri made a tepee for Little Bear. What comment did Omri's teacher make? What does this tell you about Omri?

3. Why did Patrick become annoyed with Omri at school?

4. Why did Omri bring the plastic Indian chief to life?

5. What happened to the Indian chief?

    How did Little Bear react?

How did Omri react?

6. Why did Omri's father become angry with Omri?

7. Why did Patrick buy a cowboy for Omri? What does this tell you about Patrick?

8. When Patrick finds out what the cupboard can do, what is his first thought?

Thinking About the Story:

9. Little Bear has become more demanding and bossy. Why do you think this is?

10. How do you think you would act if your parents gave you everything you asked for?

11. When Patrick suggests bringing more plastic figures to life, Omri tells him, "You couldn't just—set them up and make them do what you wanted them to. They'd do what *they* wanted to." Later Omri tells him, "it's not *fun*." Why do you think the cupboard isn't turning out to be as fun as Omri expected.

12. Look at the last line of Chapter 7. When an author ends a chapter this way, what effect does it have on the reader? What do you think will happen in the next chapter?

Dig Deeper:

13. At lunchtime, Omri broke school rules by leaving the school grounds to go to Yapp's. Read Hebrews 13:17. Do you think Omri was breaking this command when he left school grounds? Why or why not?

14. To keep Little Bear a secret, Omri lied to Patrick about whether Patrick could come over after school. Read Proverbs 6:16, 17 and 12:22. What do these verses say about how God views lying?

15. Omri stole his father's seed tray to give Little Bear a plot of ground on which to build his longhouse. Read Leviticus 6:2–5 and Ephesians 4:28. According to these verses, what is required of a person who has been stealing?

    How did Omri repay his father?

16. In order to provide for Little Bear while keeping him a secret, Omri has broken rules, lied, stolen, and even caused another person's death, although unintentionally. Read 1 Samuel 15:22, Proverbs 14:12, Proverbs 21:6, and Micah 6:6–8. Are Omri's actions justified? In other words, is it okay for him to do all these things if the end result is that Little Bear has been provided for? Explain your answer.

Optional Writing Project:

Think about the things Little Bear needed. If you were Omri, how would you provide for Little Bear without lying, stealing, or breaking rules? Would you try to keep Little Bear a secret? Write out your plan in detail.

Chapters 8, 9 & 10

Vocabulary:

For each of the following vocabulary words, write down a synonym and an antonym.

	<u>Synonym</u>	<u>Antonym</u>
1. mulish	_____	_____
2. warily	_____	_____
3. infuriated	_____	_____
4. dolefully	_____	_____
5. ornery	_____	_____
6. nonplused	_____	_____

Dialect:

A *dialect* is a regional variety of language. In this story, the spelling and grammar in the sentences spoken by Boone are written in a Western American dialect so that the reader can get a sense of the way he speaks. This can also give the reader a clue about what place and time period he is from.

Using standard spelling and grammar, rewrite the sentences below that were spoken by Boone.

Example: Ah thought Ah smelt some'n good.

I thought I smelled something good.

1. Mebbe Ah drink too much, mebbe Ah cain't hold m'likker.

2. You shore ain't no reg'lar hallucy-nation.

3. Ah jest cain't figger out what's goin' on around here.

4. That plumb ain't no ways fair.

5. Whur's mah cawfee?

6. Less'n mebbe—jest mebbe—you ain't red atall, but yeller?

Questions:

1. Why do Patrick and Omri fight?

2. Does Patrick treat Boone different from the way Omri treats Little Bear? Give some examples.

3. What does Boone think is happening to him at first?

4. How does Patrick make Omri promise to bring Boone to school?

5. Why does Little Bear want to go to school with Omri?

Thinking about the Story:

6. When Little Bear gets upset at Omri for ruining the meat, he comes after Omri with an ax. Omri stops Little Bear's rampage by threatening to put him back in the cupboard—sending him back to his own time. Why do you think Little Bear wouldn't want to go back?

7. Little Bear says to Omri, "You no Great Spirit! Only stupid boy!" How has his view of Omri changed? Is there a difference in the way he treats Omri after this incident?

8. Omri seems eager to put Boone back in the cupboard at first, but not Little Bear. Why not?

Dig Deeper:

9. Why do Boone and Little Bear dislike each other?

   Do you think it's a good reason to fight? Why or why not?

10. How does Omri attempt to make peace between Little Bear and Boone?

    Do you think this is a good way to bring about peace? Why or why not?

11. Read Matthew 5:9, Romans 14:19, and James 3:18. What is the general idea that is taught in these verses?

12. Think of a time you had a disagreement or fight with someone. What was the reason for the fight? How did you make peace again? If you have not yet made peace with the other person, write down some ways that you can bring about peace. Be willing to put these ideas into action and make peace with that person.

Chapters 11, 12 & 13

Vocabulary:

Explain the meaning of the underlined words or phrases.

1. Breakfast in his house was often a <u>dicey</u> meal anyway, with everybody more or less bad-tempered.

2. Omri had never arrived at school with more <u>apprehension in his heart</u>, not even on spelling-test days.

3. Once he had taken a white mouse to school in his <u>blazer</u> pocket.

4. "What've you got there then, what did he give you?" she asked in her <u>raucous</u> voice like a crow's.

5. Longed to bash them all one by one, or better still, all at once—a giant knocking down hordes of enemies like <u>skittles</u>.

6. Any kind of fighting or taunting, above a sly pinch or a <u>snide</u> whisper, was out.

7. Omri held his <u>persecutor</u> at eye level and shook him violently.

8. He shouted through cupped hands across the <u>yawning gulf</u> between Patrick and Omri.

9. Omri took an opportunity (when the teacher's back was turned) to open his pocket <u>stealthily</u> and peer down into it.

10. He was pleased to see them . . . apparently having a conversation, for they were both <u>gesticulating</u> with their arms.

11. The music room was not a room at all, but a little <u>alcove</u> off the gym in which the musical instruments were stored.

12. They <u>dithered about</u> for a few minutes, but it was useless to put it off, so in the end they both knocked together.

13. "This isn't small! It's tiny! It's <u>infinitesimal</u>! It's microscopic!"

Questions:

1. Why does Little Bear stab Omri during class?

2. How do Boone and Little Bear almost get squashed?

3. Write a paragraph summarizing the events that happened in Mr. Johnson's office.

4. Write a paragraph summarizing the events that happened at Yapp's.

5. What did Omri do to show Patrick that he was forgiven?

Thinking About the Story:

6. While trying to convince Boone to wash up, Omri finds himself echoing his mother. Later, when accused of stealing and hiding Adiel's football shorts, the author writes that Omri felt very far away from such babyness. What might these incidents indicate?

   What other incidents from the story indicate the same thing?

7. Little Bear asks to be pocketed along with Boone. He says "Better enemy than alone in the dark." Why do you think his attitude toward Boone has changed?

8. Why did Omri see Patrick as "not a fit person to have charge of" Boone and Little Bear?

9. Omri says to Patrick "They're not safe with you. You use them. They're people. You can't use people." How did Patrick use Boone and Little Bear?

Do you think Omri used them as well? Explain your answer using examples from the reading.

10. What is a hypocrite? Are Omri's actions in the art room hypocritical? Explain your answer.

11. Why do you think Patrick came to Omri's defense?

Dig Deeper:

12. When Patrick loudly demands that Omri hand over Little Bear and Boone, Omri sees "what happens to the nicest people when they want something badly and are determined to get it come what may." Using a concordance or topical index, find two verses from the Bible on the subject of greed, selfishness, or envy. What is the general lesson of these verses? Explain how the verses you chose relate to the story.

13. How has the relationship between Boone and Little Bear changed during this section of the reading? To what do you attribute this change?

14. Have you ever experienced a frightening, dangerous, or life-threatening situation with a friend or family member? What happened? Did your relationship, or the way you felt about that person, change at all after that incident?

15. Do you think that good things can result from dangerous situations? Explain your answer.

Chapter 14, 15 & 16

Vocabulary:

Write down the definitions of the following words. Then write a sentence using that word correctly.

1. **sheepish**
   Definition:

   Sentence:

2. **myriad**
   Definition:

   Sentence:

3. **systematically**
   Definition:

   Sentence:

4. **sieve**
   Definition:

   Sentence:

5. **trowel**
Definition:

Sentence:

6. **rapture**
Definition:

Sentence:

7. **rashly**
Definition:

Sentence:

8. **spittoons**
Definition:

Sentence:

9. **joists**
Definition:

Sentence:

10. **omnivorous**
Definition:

Sentence:

11. **albino**
    Definition:

    Sentence:

12. **penicillin**
    Definition:

    Sentence:

13. **septic**
    Definition:

    Sentence:

Questions:

1. What did Patrick and Omri discover when they got to Omri's room?

2. What lesson might Omri have learned while searching through the mess in the attic for the key.

3. How do Little Bear and Boone react when Omri tells them that he can't send them back?

Is this a change in attitude for Boone? For Little Bear? Explain.

4. The author writes that to Omri it wasn't the novelty of the cupboard that mattered anymore. "What mattered is that Little Bear should be happy." What does this tell you about Omri?

5. Why does the television show bother Little Bear?

Why does Boone enjoy the television show so much?

What happens as a result of this difference of opinion?

6. What does Little Bear's willingness to search for the key tell you about Little Bear?

7. How was the key found?

8. After the underfloor adventure is over, Omri lies awake thinking and comes to a decision. What is this decision?

   Why does he conclude that this is the right thing to do? What does this decision tell you about Omri?

Dig Deeper:

9. In his anger, Little Bear shoots Boone. Read Ecclesiastes 7:9, Ephesians 4:26, and James 1:19, 20. What do these verses say about anger?

10. What does it mean to be "slow to anger"? Was Little Bear "slow to anger" or "quickly provoked"?

11. Think of the last time you were angry with someone. What happened? Do you think you could have handled your anger better in that situation? If so, what could you have done that would have been better?

12. When Boone is revived, Little Bear humbly confesses that he shot Boone. Boone, however, continues to say insulting things to Little Bear. Although Little Bear becomes angry, Omri reminds him of what it means to be chief:

> "Chiefs ought to know how to keep their tempers! . . . Just you remember what you did—to your friend!"
> "Not friend. Enemy," muttered Little Bear. But the anger had gone out of him.
> "Whatever he is, you've got a job to do. Where are those pills? You're to see that he gets them. We can't—we can't even see them. So it's up to you!"

Read Matthew 20:25–28 and Luke 6:27–36. What is the general lesson Jesus is teaching in these verses?

13. According to these verses, what is required of Little Bear if he is to be chief?

14. Do you think Little Bear proves himself to be a proper chief? Explain using examples from the story.

15. What is Boone's general attitude toward Indians? What finally changes his attitude?

16. What do Boone and Little Bear, and later Little Bear and Omri, do to become "brothers?"

17. Read Genesis 5:1, 2 and Galatians 3:26–29. According to these verses, how are all Christians brothers and sisters?

18. Once Boone becomes Little Bear's "brother" he says "I'm part Injun! Wal . . . Ah guess Ah cain't say nothin' 'gainst 'em in the future." How can this statement apply to our relationships with our brothers and sisters in Christ?

Summary

Compare and Contrast:

How does the relationship between Omri and Little Bear compare with the relationship between God and His people? On the chart below make a compare/contrast list. Think of some things that are true of Omri's relationship with Little Bear. List these in the left column. Across from each item on the left, write down a comparable or contrasting statement that is true about God's relationship with His people. Make an equal sign (=) between the items if they show a comparison. Make slash sign (/) between the items if they show a contrast. Two have been done as an example.

Omri and Little Bear		God and His people
Omri brought Little Bear to life.	=	God put life into us.
Omri is visible. Little Bear can see him.	/	God is invisible. We cannot see Him.

Character Study:

Write a short paragraph about each of the characters listed below. Include in your paragraph answers to the following questions: Has the character changed from the beginning to the end of the story? If so, how has that character changed? What caused that change? Was it a change for the better? If you do not think the character has changed, explain your reasons.

Omri—

Little Bear—

Patrick—

Boone—

Story Structure:

1. Every work of fiction has at its root a *conflict*. The conflict is the problem that must be resolved. What is the conflict of *The Indian in the Cupboard?*

2. As a story proceeds toward its climax, a conflict can be heightened by *complications*. What complications arise in *The Indian in the Cupboard*?

3. The *climax* of a story is the high point of action or tension. It is also called the turning point because after the climax, the conflict begins to be resolved. What is the climax of *The Indian in the Cupboard*? Does there appear to be more than one climax? What might the other climax be?

4. *Resolution* occurs after the climax, when the conflict is resolved. What is the resolution of the conflict in *The Indian in the Cupboard*?

5. A *theme* is the main idea of a story. It might best be described by simply calling it the lesson the author hoped to teach her readers. What theme or themes can be found in this story?

6. How do the characters and events in the story explain this theme?

Questions:

1. Describe the relationship between Omri and his brothers.

2. Describe the relationship between the children and their parents.

3. Do you think this portrayal of family life is realistic? Explain your answer using examples from the story and from your experiences.

4. Often an author will end a story in such a way that her reader can imagine a possible continuation of the story. How is the ending of *The Indian in the Cupboard* left open for a sequel?

5. Three sequels to *The Indian in the Cupboard* have been written. (See the suggestions for further reading at the end of this guide.) But before reading these, imagine a possible sequel to this story. Write an outline of your imagined sequel. Decide what you want the theme of your story to be. Decide how you will express that idea through the characters and events of the story. Include an explanation of this in your outline. As an option, you may wish to expand your outline into a complete story.

Additional Resources

Other Books by Lynne Reid Banks:

One More River	grades 5–7, published by Avon
I, Houdini	grades 4–6, published by Avon
The Adventures of King Midas	grades 4–6, published by Avon

Other Books in the Indian in the Cupboard series:

The Return of the Indian	grades 5–7, series published by Avon
The Secret of the Indian	
The Mystery of the Cupboard	

Books of Related Interest:

The Borrowers series:

The Borrowers	series by Mary Norton, grades 4–6
The Borrowers Afield	published by Harcourt Brace & Co.
The Borrowers Afloat	
The Borrowers Aloft	
The Borrowers Avenged	
The Sign of the Beaver	by Elizabeth George Speare, grades 4–6, published by Houghton Mifflin and by Dell
The Black Stallion	by Walter Farley, grades 4–7
Bread and Butter Indian	by Anne Colver, grades 3–5, published by Holt, Rinehart & Winston

Answer Key

Chapters 1 & 2
Vocabulary:
coherent-i; plait-d; bandolier-b; intricate-h; row-f; longhouse-j; crestfallen-a; writhed-c; defiance-g; haughtily-e.

Characterization:
Accept reasonable responses for the following:
1. Omri is rather messy. He does not put his things away.
2. Omri may have a track record of losing things.
3. Omri will argue and fight about trivial things. Selfishly, he felt he should get some Rice Krispies.
4. He blames others for his own forgetfulness.
5. Omri isn't a very good speller, he doesn't study, or he doesn't care about schoolwork.
6. Omri shows that he is concerned for the well-being of someone else.
7. Omri is a little devious, trying to steal food from the kitchen rather than just asking his parents for some.

Questions:
1. Omri was disappointed. He had many plastic toys and was tired of them. He also felt that without a cowboy he couldn't really use an Indian.
2. The plastic Indian became a real, although tiny, Indian.
3. Because it was "the most marvelous thing that had ever happened to Omri," he wanted to keep it to himself and not share the experience with anyone. He was also afraid no one would believe him.
4. Answers will vary. It's hard to imagine that Little Bear, as small as he was, could possibly kill Omri.
5. Answers will vary. Sometimes experiences are more fun if we can share them with someone else. Also, when you have a secret or something that no one else has, you may feel pride about having it.
6. Luke 6:31–35: Treat others as you would have them treat you. Love not only those who love you, but your enemies as well. Romans 12:10: Love others and honor them above yourself. Put others first. Philippians 2:3: Consider others better than yourself. 1 Peter 2:17: Show respect to others; love them.
7. Answers will vary. Locking Little Bear back in the cupboard for the day is certainly mistreatment, although Little Bear didn't seem to mind. Just grabbing him without warning was mistreatment as well. But Omri's attempts to provide for Little Bear show his concern for Little Bear's welfare.

Chapters 3, 4 & 5
Vocabulary:
1. gracefully; 2. two or more squads of soldiers operating together; 3. the upper front part of a saddle; 4. in British usage, any truck; 5. unwilling, hesitant; 6. apprehension, anxiety, fear; 7. a piece of cloth or other device tied tightly around a wounded limb to stop the flow of blood.

Questions:
1. The plastic tepee had become a real, but tiny, tepee. The matchbox car remained a toy, made of metal. Answers will vary. The first time Omri did not lock the door, so it appears that the key is an important part of making the plastic objects real.
2. It bothers Omri because it means that Little Bear is not a toy, but a real person who has somehow been transported through time to his cupboard. He has fought in wars and has killed people. Little Bear may be dangerous to have around. He will need to be treated like a real person. Omri will not be able to control him. Answers will vary. Perhaps Omri gives Little Bear more respect. He provides Little Bear with food, tools, a horse, and takes him outside to ride the horse, but Omri may have done these things for Little Bear anyway.
3. While carrying Little Bear and the horse back into the house, Omri runs into his father. When Omri clutches the box in surprise, the horse becomes frightened and kicks Little Bear.
4. Omri brings cotton and Listerine as an antiseptic. To get tiny bandages, Omri brings a WWI field medic to life who binds Little Bear's wound.
5. To get an axe for Little Bear, Omri brings to life a knight holding a battle-axe, snatches the axe from his hands, and turns him back to plastic.

6. Answers will vary. Little Bear seems to give Omri god-like status, recognizing that Omri is someone who can provide him with the things he needs. Little Bear accepts it when Omri refuses him things.

7. Little Bear keeps on asking Omri for things. Omri has become his provider.

8. Little Bear asks for paint, longhouse, meat, gun, a herd of horses, a place to ride the horse, bow, arrows, club, water, cloths, tree bark, earth, posts, tools, pots, and fire.

9. No. Omri gives Little Bear a tepee, meat, *one* horse, a place to ride it, antiseptic, cotton, tree bark, twigs, soil in a seed tray, and an axe. Omri refuses to give Little Bear *all* the horses and a gun.

10. Little Bear is disappointed, but simply accepts it when Omri refuses to give him some things.

11. Answers will vary. Even though we think we know what is good for us to have, God knows what is best for us.

12. God is willing to give good things to his children. Psalm 84:11 says "to those whose walk is blameless," indicating that righteousness is required of us if we wish to receive anything from God. Remember, however, that all people are guilty of sin, and Christ had to provide our righteousness. First of all we must ask, and we must ask according to his will.

13. Three times Paul asked God to take away some sort of affliction which he called "a thorn in my flesh." God, however, told Paul that His grace was sufficient and His power is made perfect in weakness. Paul said it was so that he would not be conceited. Paul responded by saying that he could then delight in weaknesses and hardships.

14. Jesus prayed that he might not have to be crucified. It was God's will that Jesus go to the cross. Jesus said "not as I will, but as you will." He humbly obeyed.

15. Answers will vary.

Point of View:

1. the sun, or a huge oil lamp.

2. the ground, or a blanket.

3. huge boulders.

4. trees.

5. "an escarpment twice the height of a man."

6. a huge bird of prey.

Chapters 6 & 7
Vocabulary:

1. corn; 2. pennies; 3. irritable; 4. urgent; 5. intimidate; 6. shocked; 7. reach; 8. expectant; 9. generously; 10. weak; 11. odor.

Questions:

1. Answers will vary. Iroquois Indians were sometimes called "The Five Nations." They lived in longhouses. Their main foods were maize, squash, and beans. These vegetables were called "The Three Sisters." The Algonquins were the enemies of the Iroquois. the Iroquois fought with the English during the French and Indian War. Scalping was introduced to the Indians by the Europeans.

2. Omri's teacher said "Very good, Omri! What patience all of a sudden!" indicating that Omri was not known for his patience in handicrafts class.

3. Patrick became annoyed with Omri because Omri kept talking about Little Bear without actually telling Patrick what had happened to the plastic Indian.

4. Omri brought the Indian chief to life so that Little Bear could have his bow and arrows.

5. It's not clear, but the Indian chief apparently suffered a heart attack from the fright of seeing Omri. Little Bear accepted simply the death and began to take the chief's cloak, weapons, and headdress. Omri was shocked at Little Bear's behavior and apparent lack of respect for the dead.

6. Omri's father discovered that his seed tray was missing and that someone had stripped bark from the birch tree.

7. Patrick bought a cowboy for Omri so that he could "play a proper game with the Indian." Patrick seems to have done this as a way to make up with Omri for being annoyed with him at school. He shows that his friendship with Omri is important to him.

8. Patrick's first thought is to bring lots of other plastic figures to life—whole armies.

9. Answers will vary. One reason might be that Omri has willingly given Little Bear almost everything he wants, so Little Bear keeps asking. Another reason might be that now that Little Bear has made himself chief he wants to be served.

10. Answers will vary. Being spoiled, a person might become as bossy as Little Bear.

11. Answers will vary. Omri expected to have control over the plastic figures even after they came to life. Unfortunately Little Bear has a will of his own. Omri cannot control him.

12. Answers will vary. Ending a chapter in this fashion makes a reader want to read on. Answers will vary.

13. Answers will vary. The school rules were made by the teachers and other authorities at school. Omri was disobeying this command by disobeying the rules.

14. According to these verses, God hates lying.

15. Answers will vary. According to these verses, one who is stealing should stop stealing and repay the person he stole from. After Omri's father discovered the theft, Omri bought another seed tray for his father, filled it will soil, and also brought some extra seeds for his him.

16. Answers will vary. No, Omri's actions are not justified. He may think that he is doing right, but according to these and other verses in this section, his actions are clearly wrong. Wrong actions, even done for a good cause, are still wrong.

Chapters 8, 9 & 10
Vocabulary:
Accept reasonable responses.
1. syn. stubborn, obstinate, ornery; ant. willing, eager, compliant.
2. syn. cautiously, carefully, discreetly; ant. rashly, recklessly.
3. syn. angered, provoked, enraged; ant. soothed, calmed.
4. syn. mournfully, sadly, unhappily; ant. happily, gladly, cheerfully.
5. syn. mean, stubborn, obstinate; ant. friendly, willing, compliant.
6. syn. perplexed, confounded, baffled; ant. certain, assured.

Dialect:
Accept Reasonable Responses.
1. Maybe I drink too much, maybe I can't hold my liquor.
2. You sure aren't a regular hallucination.
3. I just can't figure out what's going on around here.
4. That's not fair, or That just isn't fair.
5. Where's my coffee?
6. Unless maybe—just maybe—you aren't red at all, but yellow?

Questions:
1. Patrick wanted to bring another plastic figure to life. Omri wanted to stop him, or at least make him think about the consequences first.

2. Yes. Patrick does not seem to consider Boone as a real person but as a plaything, whereas Omri treats Little Bear with great respect. Patrick handles Boone and the horse roughly. Patrick keeps distant from Boone, merely watching Boone and his horse struggle across the quilt without helping. Omri helps Little Bear deal with his new environment. Patrick is not careful with Boone and the horse, simply scooping them into his pocket. Omri made a little box for carrying Little Bear and his horse.

3. Boone thinks he is having delirium tremens—alcohol-related hallucinations.

4. Patrick threatens to tell everyone about the cupboard if Omri does not bring Boone to school.

5. Omri tells Little Bear that it would be risky and dangerous to take him to school. The promise of danger, however, strengthens Little Bear's desire to go.

6. Answers will vary. Little Bear has an easy life with Omri. In Omri's world he is chief, everything he wants is provided to him, there is a new world to explore, and there is danger and excitement. Perhaps for these reasons Little Bear would rather stay.

7. Answers will vary. Little Bear no longer views Omri as some sort of god or supernatural being. He realizes that Omri is just a boy. Perhaps there is some change in the way he treats Omri. After this incident Little Bear either orders Omri around or tries to reason with Omri to get the things he wants.

8. Answers will vary. Although Omri feels it would be best to send Boone back to his own time for Boone's own good, he still feels some ownership of Little Bear and does not want to give him up even though it would probably be best for Little Bear. Omri's attitude in this matter is still somewhat selfish.

9. Little Bear dislikes Boone merely because he is a white man, and white men took Indian lands. Boone dislikes Little Bear merely because he is an Indian. Answers will vary. It's not a good reason to fight. They fight out of blind prejudice. Their dislike of each other is racially motivated and has nothing to do with who they are personally. Each is reducing the other to a stereotype.

10. Omri forces them to eat breakfast together. Food is a basic human need. Omri is hoping their desire for food will outweigh their desire for vengeance. Answers will vary.

11. God desires that we work to bring about peace. The result, according to James 3:18 is a "harvest of righteousness."

12. Answers will vary.

Chapters 11, 12 & 13
Vocabulary:

1. risky, a gamble; 2. a sense of uneasiness or fear; 3. an informal sport coat or jacket; 4. harsh, rough-sounding; 5. the pins in an English game similar to bowling; 6. slyly belittling; 7. one who annoys, oppresses, or harasses; 8. a very large, open space, 9. with secrecy; 10. gesturing while speaking; 11. a small recess or partially enclosed section of a room; 12. acted with indecision or agitation; 13. immeasurably small.

Questions:

1. Little Bear is tired of being in Omri's pocket where it is dark and hard to breathe. He wants to see the school and *enjoy* the experience.

2. They are together in Patrick's pocket when he is pushed from his chair and lands on the floor.

3. Paragraphs will vary somewhat but should contain the following information: Mr. Johnson questions Patrick and Omri. Patrick starts giggling uncontrollably when Mr. Johnson asks if someone stuck a knife in Omri. In this state, Omri fears that Patrick will tell Mr. Johnson about Boone and Little Bear. Mr. Johnson threatens to call Patrick's father. Fear of his father makes Patrick tell Mr. Johnson about Little Bear. Just before Patrick takes Boone and Little Bear out of his pocket Omri tackles him. Omri is dragged from the office. Patrick does show the little men to Mr. Johnson who turns white and goes home sick.

4. Omri took Little Bear and Boone out of his pocket to let Little Bear pick an Indian woman for himself. Omri buys the plastic Indian woman, but Mr. Yapp accuses Omri of stealing a cowboy and an Indian. Omri claims innocence. Patrick appears at Omri's side and vouches for him. Omri whispers to the little men to lie still and shows them to Mr. Yapp. Mr. Yapp sees that these are different men from the ones he has in his store and apologizes to Omri.

5. Omri let Patrick spend the night and watch when they brought the Indian woman to life.

6. Answers will vary. These incidents may indicate that Omri was beginning to understand the responsibilities that go along with taking care of someone. It makes him feel grownup, and it helps him understand what his parents must have to put up with. Other incidents from the story: When Little Bear was wounded Omri did what he'd seen his mother do for antiseptic. He used his father's tone-of-voice when Boone and Little Bear fought. The worry that Omri constantly felt about the little men was beginning to wear him out.

7. Little Bear recognizes the need for human companionship. In a dark and strange place he wants to have *someone* with him, even Boone.

8. Patrick didn't seem to understand that Boone and Little Bear were not toys, but were real people. He continued to treat them as *things*.

9. Patrick used them as a novelty—something for fun. He handled them roughly, stuffing them into his pocket. He used them to prove his story to Mr. Johnson. Answers will vary. Omri certainly used Little Bear as something for fun. But in general he honored the requests of the little men. Earlier when he asked if Little Bear wanted another Indian brought to life, Little Bear said no. Omri honored this because he felt he couldn't do anything Little Bear didn't want. Instead of trying to force Little Bear and Boone to do what he wanted them to do, he tried to provide for them and let them do what they wished.

10. A hypocrite is someone who advocates beliefs and attitudes he does not adhere to himself. Answers will vary. His actions may be seen as hypocritical. Immediately after telling Patrick not to *use* Boone and Little Bear because they were people, Omri used them for a bit of fun in the art room.

11. Answers will vary. Patrick may have felt that he owed Omri the favor of coming to his defense after their disagreement at school. It was a way for Patrick to show that he was sorry.

12. Verses will vary. Some possibilities: Psalm 10:2, 3, Ecclesiastes 4:4, James 3:14–16, Luke 12:15, Ephesians 5:3, Philippians 2:4.

13. Boone and Little Bear began as enemies, but they seem to have become friends by the end of this section of reading. Answers will vary. Because they only had each other to rely on, the dangerous and frightening situation at school caused the two of them to draw closer together.

14. Answers will vary.

15. Answers will vary. They can teach us to rely on each other, to rely on God, to see what is really important in life, etc.

Chapters 14, 15 & 16
Vocabulary:

1. embarrassed and apologetic; 2. constituting a very large, indefinite number; 3. methodically, by procedure; 4. an instrument of wire mesh used for straining, draining, or sifting; 5. a small gardening tool with a scoop-shaped blade; 6. a state of ecstacy; 7. hastily, without caution or thought; 8. a vessel for spitting into; 9. parallel horizontal beams set wall to wall to support a floor or ceiling; 10. eating both plant and animal matter; 11. a person or animal with a deficiency of pigment in the skin, hair and eyes; 12. an antibiotic used to treat or prevent a wide variety of diseases; 13. infected, forming pus, resulting in blood poisoning.

Questions:

1. The cupboard was gone. Adiel had stolen it and had hidden it in the attic.

2. Omri might have learned the importance of keeping things neat and tidy and in their proper place.

3. They are not happy with the news. As much as they seem to enjoy their adventure through the cupboard, they both realize what it means to never go back to their own time periods. Both were given very special treatment. Boone didn't seem to enjoy being in Omri's world very much right from the start. It's a clear change in attitude for Little Bear, who seemed to enjoy being chief by virtue of being the only Indian in Omri's world.

4. This indicates that Omri is more concerned with Little Bear's welfare than his own. As much as he'd like to keep Little Bear, Omri wants to give Little Bear what Little Bear wants.

5. The television show bothers Little Bear because it shows Indians being killed by white settlers. Boone enjoys the television show for the same reason. Little Bear becomes upset with Boone's insults and finally shoots him with an arrow.

6. This indicates that Little Bear is sorry for what he did to Boone.

7. The key had fallen beneath the floorboards in Omri's bedroom. When one board was lifted up, Little Bear went down into the floor to search for the key. Little Bear found the key and was pulled from the hole seconds before Gillon's rat got him.

8. He decides that it would be best to send Little Bear and Boone back to their own times. He kept imagining that no matter what happened, it would end in some sort of disaster. This decision indicates that Omri is becoming less selfish—that he is willing to lay aside his own desires for the well-being of others.

9. These verses do not say that anger is a sin, but they do indicate that anger is not a good thing. It does not bring about righteousness.

10. To be slow to anger means to not get angry quickly or act rashly. Although he didn't shoot Boone immediately, Little Bear was probably "quickly provoked."

11. Answers will vary.

12. Jesus is teaching that if you want to be great, you need to be a servant—giving to all regardless of their actions and without expecting any repayment.

13. If Little Bear is to be chief he must be a servant—serving both friends and enemies.

14. Answers will vary. Even though he considers Boone his enemy, Little Bear goes under the floor and into danger to get the key. Even though Boone continues to insult him, Little Bear takes care of him and watches over him.

15. Boone's general attitude toward Indians is that they are all murderous savages. His attitude changes only after he and Little Bear become blood brothers. He says that now that he is part Indian, he can no longer say anything bad about them.

16. To become brothers they make cuts on their skin, tie the open wounds together, and let the blood mingle. Considering that there are many blood-borne diseases, this is a dangerous practice.

17. All people are made in the image of God. In that sense all people are "related." The verses in Galatians say that all who have faith in Jesus are children of God, therefore brothers and sisters, descendants of Abraham and heirs to the Kingdom of God. Galatians 3:28 could also read "there is neither cowboy nor Indian."

18. Answers will vary. Galatians 3:28 says there is neither Jew nor Greek, slave nor free, male nor female, for we are all one in Christ. If we are all one in Christ, then there's no room for quarrels or disagreements among us because no one would be better than another.

Summary
Compare and Contrast:
You may wish to do this exercise as a class discussion. Some other possibilities are: Omri provides for Little Bear = God provides for his people. Omri does not control Little Bear. Little Bear has free will = God gave his people free will. Omri does not give Little Bear everything he wants = God does not give us everything we want. Little Bear discovered that Omri was only a boy ≠ We know that God is a holy and perfect God.
Character Study:
Answers will vary. In general: Omri has become less selfish, more giving. Little Bear has become less bossy and temperamental, more of a servant. Patrick has come to understand that the little men are really people. He is less selfish also. Boone no longer insults Little Bear because of the blood brother ritual, but otherwise he hasn't really changed. Accept other reasonable responses.
Story Structure:
1. Answers will vary. The conflict in the *Indian in the Cupboard* is how Omri attempts to provide for Little Bear and have some fun with him while trying to protect him and keep him a secret.
2. Answers will vary. Complications to this conflict may include: Little Bear's many needs, his injury, his selfish attitude, letting Patrick in on the secret, bringing Boone to life, taking the little men to school, the missing key, and Boone's injury.
3. Answers will vary. The climax occurs when Boone lies dying and Little Bear must go below the floor to retrieve the key. It could be said that there is more than one climax. Another climax takes place in Mr. Johnson's office when Omri's and Patrick's friendship is put to the test. If a student indicates that the main conflict of the book is the state of Omri's and Patrick's friendship, then this would be the major climax.
4. Answers will vary. The resolution of the conflict is that Omri realizes there is no way he can safely keep Little Bear and Boone in his world. He sends them back to their own time periods.
5. Answers will vary. The main theme appears to be to treat others with the respect they deserve, or the golden rule: Do to others as you would have them do to you. (Luke 6:31)
6. Answers will vary. The relationships between most of the characters, major and minor, all need some kind of repair. Omri and his brothers fight. Omri and Patrick fight. Little Bear and Boone fight. Patrick mistreats Boone. Most of the characters are marked by a certain degree of selfishness. We can see in the story how these attitudes bring about more problems. Only after harmony comes to these relationships do we see things start to turn around.
Questions:
1. Omri and his brothers fight over very minor things. They are not kind to each other.
2. The constant bickering of the children is a burden to their mother. The parents, however, seem to love their children in spite of the trouble they cause.
3. Answers will vary based on students' experience.
4. The cupboard will bring back Little Bear, Bright Stars, and Boone any time Omri and Patrick wish it. The key is in the safe keeping of Omri's mother.
5. Discuss the importance of planning a story using an outline before actually beginning to write it.